WHICH HAT TODAY?

Margaret Ballinger and Rachel Gosset
illustrated by Janet Wolf

Copyright © 1996 by Scholastic Australia Pty Limited.
All rights reserved. Published by Scholastic Inc., 555 Broadway, New York, NY 10012
by arrangement with Scholastic Australia Pty Limited.
Printed in the U.S.A.

ISBN 0-439-11668-6

SCHOLASTIC, READING DISCOVERY, and associated logos and
designs are trademarks and/or registered trademarks of Scholastic Inc.

1 2 3 4 5 6 7 8 9 10   08   06 05 04 03 02 01 00 99

SCHOLASTIC INC.
New York Toronto London Auckland Sydney
Mexico City New Delhi Hong Kong

Which hat will I wear today?

rainy

windy

sunny

cold

Which hat will I wear today?
It's a rainy day.
This is the hat I'll wear today.

Which hat will I wear today?
It's a sunny day.
This is the hat I'll wear today.

Which hat will I wear today?
It's a windy day.
This is the hat I'll wear today.

Which hat will I wear today?
It's a cold day.
This is the hat I'll wear today.

Which hat will I wear today?
It's my birthday.
This is the hat I'll wear today.